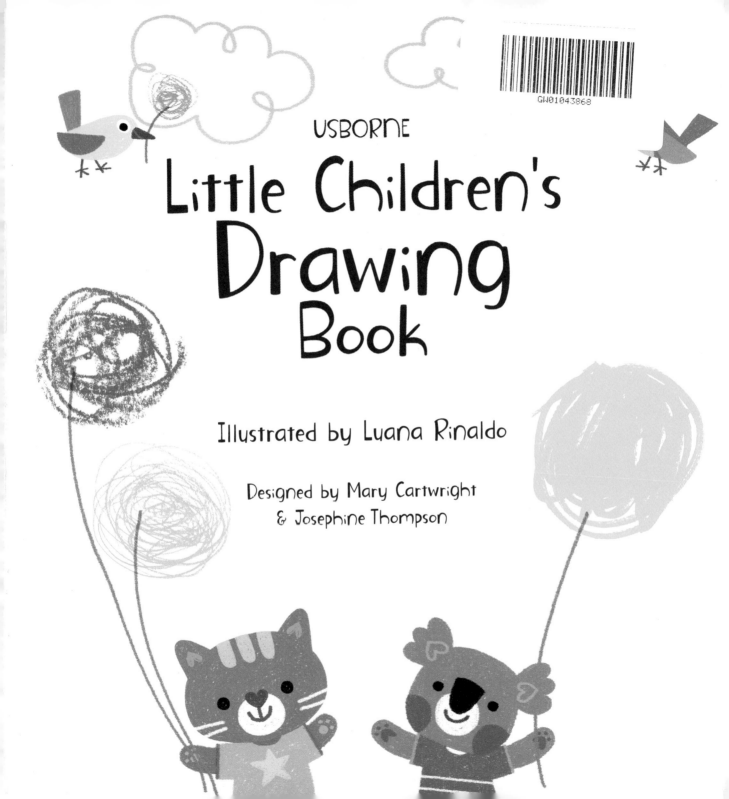

USBORNE

Little Children's Drawing Book

Illustrated by Luana Rinaldo

Designed by Mary Cartwright
& Josephine Thompson

GW01043868

Please draw circles round the socks.

We all need wheels! Please draw some for us.

Bees need flowers.

Draw flowers on all the stems.

What colours will you choose?

We need more lily pads so we can hop around!

I'm a hip, hoppy frog.

There's lots of space.

Race around the track with red and blue lines.

Vrrroom vroom...

Help me draw circles round these bugs.

Notes for grown-ups

The drawing activities in this book encourage little children to try out all sorts of different marks, giving them lots of practice holding and manipulating a pen or pencil. This helps them develop the pen control skills that are essential for learning to write and draw.

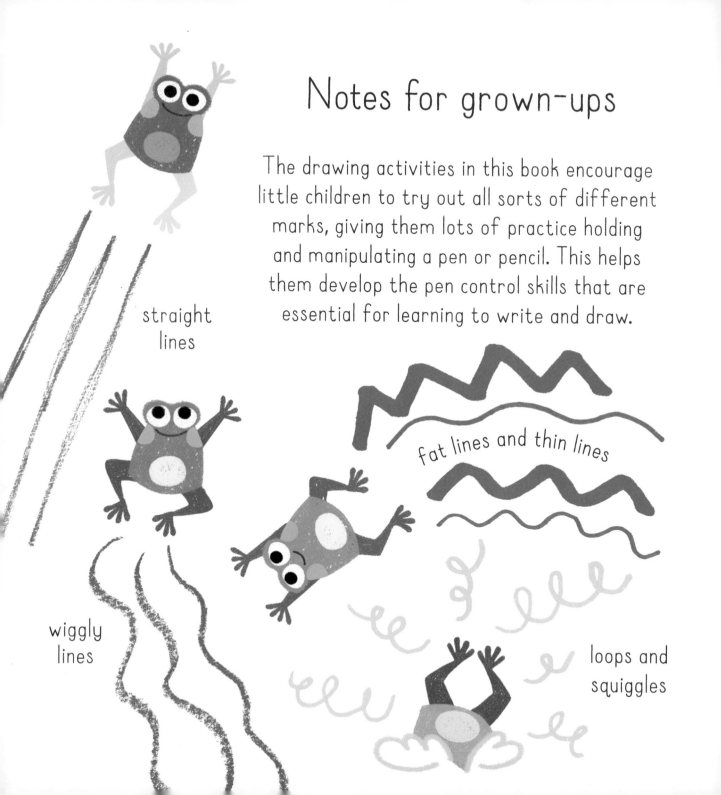

straight lines

fat lines and thin lines

wiggly lines

loops and squiggles

Help children get started by giving them bright wax crayons, pencils or washable felt-tip pens of varying thicknesses, suitable for small hands.

Let children experiment with the drawing tools, trying out different marks as they respond to the lively pictures on each page.

dots, circles and swirls

Edited by Jenny Tyler

With thanks to young helpers Maya, Natalia, Theo, Ruby,
Arran, Liam, Abigail, Edward, Elon and Harry for testing activities.